for Connor, Landon
and Reese ...

Praying you will follow
Jesus with your whole heart!
And, when life is hard ...
imagine Heaven!

Betsy deArmas

The Heaven of My Fancy

...Happy Thoughts for Sad Days

written by Betsy de Armas
art by Betsy de Armas and Laura Creeden

First Printing, 2015

ISBN-13: 978-1682730256
ISBN-10: 1682730255

The text in this book is InkyDoo Serif by Joebob Graphics.

Printed in China by onthemark.net

1 Corinthians 2:9
"No eye has seen, no ear has heard,
no mind has conceived
the things God has prepared
for those who love him"

... BUT, we can imagine!

FOR SHILOH
...never forget...
"Happy loves you
and Jesus loves you!"

There's a home that I long
for yet I've never been
in the Bible it's written,
beginning to end.
We may find little tidbits
and glimpses on earth,
yet there's much left to ponder
of Heaven's great worth.

HEAVEN

Now I sit and I wonder,
God's Word as my guide,
what this Heaven would be like
if I could decide.
Of celestial enjoyment
I've written a list.
this dear Heaven of my fancy
would sure look like this:

No more homesickness, goodbyes, no aches of the heart,
any illness and aging would play not a part.
All the loneliness, bitterness, sadness and such
wouldn't have any chance to give my soul a touch.

Loving parents would not see kids march off to war,
no more fear of the army chaplain at their door.
The abusers, and thieves, murderers, and the like,
they will bring no terror in the land of no night.

No more battles of flesh and mind, no fears nor tests,
those things that we struggle with are all put to rest.
And the minds that are lost and are jumbled and old
will be put back together and brilliant as gold.

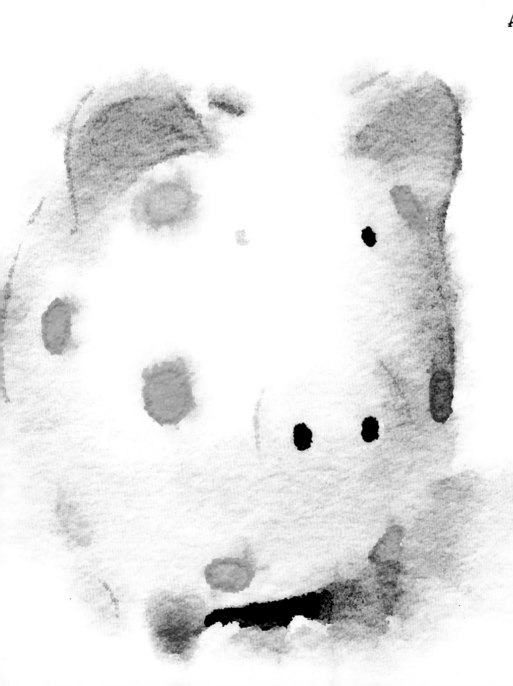

All our finances,
taxes, our debt
and our greed,
they will not
have a place
where there's
never a need.
And the
rush hour,
time clocks,
and schedules
and schemes,
they will take
a backseat
to our
unhurried
dreams.

But this Heaven of my fancy is more than "no mores."
It's a list of the happiness we'll find galore.
Though I'll mention a few to whet our appetites,
it will be more superb when our faith turns to sight.

I will start with the family we've lost through the years,
for to see them so perfect will bring forth loud cheers.
We'll sit back on the porch, endless time there to chat.
Could you ever imagine thoughts better than that?

All our friends that we've lost and have loved in the past
will all be there, and we will start catching up fast.
We'll remember the fun and the mischief as well
and start laughing again, catching up will be swell!

And those
sweet little pets
that we cared for
down here,
there in Heaven
they wait
for their masters
so dear.
They will
wag their cute tails
as their ears
perk up straight;
when we call out
their names,
they will
run to the gate.

As for music,
it will be a must in that land,
never crude, never nasty,
or sad, dull, or bland.
Every instrument
of every musical style,
just the mere thought of it,
that really makes me smile!

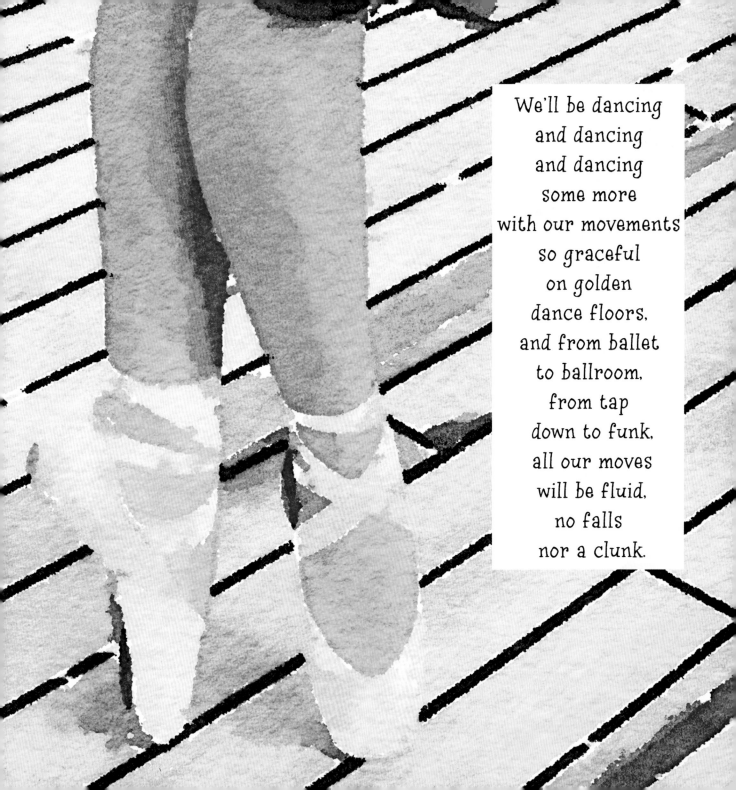

We'll be dancing
and dancing
and dancing
some more
with our movements
so graceful
on golden
dance floors,
and from ballet
to ballroom,
from tap
down to funk,
all our moves
will be fluid,
no falls
nor a clunk.

About food you may ask,
let's just get this one straig
there will never, no never,
be more empty plates.
With our bellies so full,
we will all have enough,
and forever we'll taste
and enjoy yummy stuff.

Do you wonder
what drinks
we'll enjoy
when we dine?
Our Lord Jesus
is vintner,
and He makes
the wine.
That was His first
miraculous work
He did here,
and He still
makes it best
never matter
the year.

Do you love to climb mountains, or sit at the beach?
Well, in Heaven we will have them both within reach.
Do you like colder weather or wish it were hot?
Well, in Heaven there's choices for your perfect spot.

Pretty flowers and trees and green plants will abound;
they will flourish and thrive with no weeds to surround.
Flowing rivers and lakes, quiet ponds, even creeks;
many waters to love, any kind that you seek.

Countless houses to live in, and ones to enjoy;
there will never be homeless or sad girls and boys.
You'll find big ones and small ones of stone and of brick,
and whatever your fancy, you can have your pick.

For eternity,
what will we do,
you might say,
"Will we sit 'round
and play
golden harps
everyday?"
Well, of course not,
God has special jobs
we will do,
nothing dull,
nothing boring,
one made
just for you.

Our God
is our Creator,
He knows
how we tick;
we will love
what we do
and the time
will pass quick!
Although
it will not matter,
there will
be no clocks,
no more counting
the days,
the years,
tick tock tick tock!

All these thoughts
are so lovely
to wonder about,
but the best thing
in Heaven,
without any doubt
will be Jesus
there waiting
for us to embrace;
we will
finally see Him,
our Amazing Grace.

Oh, the Heaven of my fancy's a wonderful place,
but to write it all down, I'd sure run out of space;
because no eye has seen, no mind can comprehend,
yet His children know it will be Eden again!

What is the Heaven of YOUR fancy?

Acknowledgements

This book was inspired by a "homework" project for my weekly Bible study group. We were studying *Don't Cry Past Tuesday* by Charles E. Poole, a wonderful book containing quotes from a sermon in which a pastor describes the "Heaven of his fancy." So, our assignment was to write a list of the things we hope to find, or not find, in Heaven if it were up to us. As I started to make my list, it began to flow in the rhythm of a poem. It was especially poignant to me at this point in my life because my mother had just been diagnosed with dementia. I needed to be reminded that better days lie ahead and that this life is so short in the scope of eternity. Jesus fixes everything there that is broken here!

I began to read the poem, often just to encourage myself on sad days. I was also inspired by a children's book, *Dog Heaven* by Cynthia Rylant, of which I have bought many copies over the years to give to both children and adults when they lose a dear pet. I began to have conversations with our young grandson about Heaven and what it will be like. My heart was full as I watched his imagination soar during these talks. And so, the idea came that this poem would be great in book form to be shared with others, young and old, when sadness and grief are upon them. I hope you find some "happy" on sad days. This life is not the end... it is the beginning!

Special Thanks

Laura Creeden, for helping me with the artwork and creative design. I owe you for life!

Courtney Caggiano, for the edit and teaching me all about anapestic tetrameter!

My Bible Study Babes: Danielle, Janet, Jennifer, Laura, Sara and Suzie, for coming up with the homework assignment that inspired this book, and for sharing life and encouragement—week in and week out!

Danny, my husband extraordinaire, sounding board, and Sugar Daddy, love you, love you, love you!

My sweet mom, Jeanette Henry, for showing me that even in the midst of dementia, in her very core and deepest part of her brain and heart, Jesus lives. She still knows Him and honors Him—even when she confuses and forgets the ones closest to her. The thought of Heaven is even dearer to me now as I anticipate that day when she will be young and beautiful and brilliant again!

To purchase more books, visit
www.heavenofmyfancy.com